Year 5 Assessing Pupil Progress in Mathematics (APP)
Photocopiable Activity Book

C000203906

Introduction

Using the assessment statements outlined on the Primary National Strategy Assessing Pupils Progress Guidelines (reproduced under licence at the beginning of this book) this series of books provides carefully organised assessments for each area of the mathematics curriculum. The activities can be used to determine the level a pupil is working at. They can also be used to indicate gaps in learning.

There is a book for each year group from Year1 – Year 6 aimed at pupils aged 6 to 11. When a written test is completed, an easy to carry out assessment of AT1 (Using and Applying Mathematics) is provided to enable a National Curriculum level to be determined (e.g. Level 3b). The tests are compiled in such a way that a Level 3b would be exactly the same whether achieved on a Y1, Y4 or Y6 assessment.

For each year group there are differentiated assessments aimed at pupils of different abilities.

In this Year 5 book there are assessments for:

Level 3 = Lower Ability
Level 4 = Average Ability
Level 5 = Higher Ability

The assessments within this book can be used as a baseline test or used at the end of a term to assess progress.

Contents

Topical Resources publishes a range of Educational Materials for use in Primary Schools and Pre-School Nurseries and Playgroups.

Copyright © 2010 Helen Maden
First Published January 2010.
ISBN: 978-1-907269-13-4

Illustrated by John Hutchinson,
Art Works, Fairhaven, 69 Worden Lane,
Leyland, Preston

Designed by Paul Sealey, PS3 Creative,
3 Wentworth Drive, Thornton, Lancashire.

Printed in the UK for 'Topical Resources'
by T. Snape and Co Ltd., Boltons Court,
Preston, Lancashire.

For the latest catalogue
Tel 01772 863158
Fax 01772 866153
email: sales@topical-resources.co.uk

Visit our Website at:
www.topical-resources.co.uk

Mathematics Attainment Target 1 (MA 1) Using and Applying Mathematics

Level 5 (L5)

Problem solving

A identify and obtain necessary information to carry through a task and solve mathematical problems, e.g.
- recognise information that is important to solving the problem, determine what is missing and develop lines of enquiry
- break a several-step problem or investigation into simpler steps
- consider efficient methods, relating problems to previous experiences

B check results, considering whether these are reasonable, e.g.
- check as they work, spotting and correcting errors and reviewing methods

C solve word problems and investigations from a range of contexts, e.g.
- use mathematical content from levels 4 and 5 to solve problems and investigate

Communicating

A present information and results in a clear and organised way, e.g.
- organise written work, e.g. record results in order
- begin to work in an organised way from the start
- consider appropriate units
- use related vocabulary accurately

Reasoning

A draw simple conclusions of their own and give an explanation of their reasoning, e.g.
- explain and justify their methods and solution
- identify more complex patterns, making generalisations in words and begin to express generalisations using symbolic notation
- use examples and counter-examples to justify conclusions

Level 4 (L4)

Problem solving

A develop own strategies for solving problems, e.g.
- make their own suggestions of ways to tackle a range of problems
- make connections to previous work
- pose and answer questions related to a problem
- check answers and ensure solutions make sense in the context of the problem
- review their work and approaches

B use their own strategies within mathematics and in applying mathematics to practical context
- use mathematical content from levels 3 and 4 to solve problems and investigate

Communicating

A show understanding of situations by describing them mathematically using symbols, words and diagrams, e.g.
- organise their work from the outset, looking for ways to record systematically
- decide how best to represent conclusions, using appropriate recording
- begin to understand and use formulae and symbols to represent problems

Reasoning

A search for a solution by trying out ideas of their own, e.g.
- check their methods and justify answers
- identify patterns as they work and form their own generalisations/rules in words

Level 3 (L3)

Problem solving

A select the mathematics they use in a wider range of classroom activities, e.g.
- use classroom discussions to break into a problem, recognising similarities to previous work
- put the problem into their own words
- use mathematical content from levels 2 and 3
- choose their own equipment appropriate to the task, including calculators

B try different approaches and find ways of overcoming difficulties that arise when they are solving problems, e.g.
- check their work and make appropriate corrections, e.g. decide that two numbers less than 100 cannot give a total more than 200 and correct the addition
- begin to look for patterns in results as they work and use them to find other possible outcomes

Communicating

A begin to organise their work and check results, e.g.
- begin to develop own ways of recording
- develop an organised approach as they get into recording their work on a problem

B discuss their mathematical work and begin to explain their thinking, e.g.
- use appropriate mathematical vocabulary
- talk about their findings by referring to their written work

C use and interpret mathematical symbols and diagrams

Reasoning

A understand a general statement by finding particular examples that match it, e.g.
- make a generalisation with the assistance of probing questions and prompts

B review their work and reasoning, e.g.
- respond to 'What if?' questions
- when they have solved a problem, pose a similar problem for a partner

Mathematics Attainment Target 2 (MA 2) Number and Algebra

Level 5 (L5)

system

A use understanding of place value to multiply and divide whole numbers and decimals by 10, 100 and 1000 and explain the effect
B round decimals to the nearest decimal place
C order negative numbers in context
D recognise and use number patterns and relationships, e.g.
- find two-digit prime numbers
- make generalisations about sequences saying whether much larger numbers will be in the sequence or not

percentages, ratio & proportion

A use equivalence between fractions, e.g.
- convert fractions such as 2/5 into tenths or hundredths and express them as decimals or percentages and vice versa
B reduce a fraction to its simplest form by cancelling common factors
C order fractions and decimals, e.g.
- order fractions with different denominators
- order decimals that have a mixture of one, two or three decimal places
D understand simple ratio

between them

A use known facts, place value and knowledge of operations to calculate, e.g.
- calculate decimal complements to 10 or 100, such as 100 - 63.8
- multiply a two-digit number by a single digit, e.g. 39 × 7
- calculate simple fractions or percentages of a number/quantity, e.g. 3/8 of 400g or 60% of £300
B apply inverse operations
C use brackets appropriately, e.g.
- know and use the order of operations, including brackets

A solve simple problems involving ordering, adding, subtracting negative numbers in context
B solve simple problems involving ratio and direct proportion, e.g.
- begin to use multiplication rather than trial and improvement to solve ratio problems
C approximate to check answers to problems are of the correct magnitude
D use a calculator where appropriate to calculate fractions/percentages of quantities/measurements, e.g.
- find fractions of quantities such as 3/8 of 980
- find percentages such as 15% of 360g
E understand and use an appropriate noncalculator method for solving problems that involve multiplying and dividing any threedigit number by any two-digit number

A add and subtract negative numbers in context
B estimate using approximations
C use all four operations with decimals to two places, e.g.
- add and subtract numbers that do not have the same number of decimal places
- multiply or divide decimal numbers by a single digit, e.g. 31.62 × 7

A construct, express in symbolic form, and use simple formulae involving one or two operations, e.g.
- understand simple expressions using symbols e.g. '2 less than n' can be written as 'n - 2'
- evaluate expressions by substituting numbers into them
- use symbols to represent an unknown number or a variable
B use and interpret coordinates in all four quadrants

Level 4 (L4)

Numbers and the number system

A recognise and describe number patterns, e.g.
- continue sequences involving decimals
B recognise and describe number relationships including multiple, factor and square
C use place value to multiply and divide whole numbers by 10 or 100

Fractions, decimals, percentages, & ratio

A recognise approximate proportions of a whole and use simple fractions and percentages to describe these
- recognise simple equivalence between fractions, decimals and percentages e.g. 1/2, 1/4, 1/10, 3/4
- convert mixed numbers to improper fractions and vice versa
B order decimals to threedecimal places
C begin to understand simple ratio

Operations, relationships between them

A use inverse operations, e.g.
- use a calculator and inverse operations to find missing numbers, including decimals
- 'undo' two-step problems including those using division, such as 20 + __ = 100 ÷ 4
B understand the use of brackets in simple calculations
C quickly derive division facts that correspond to multiplication facts up to 10 × 10

Mental methods

A use a range of mental methods of computation with the four operations, e.g.
- calculate complements to 1000
B recall multiplication facts up to 10 × 10 and quickly derive corresponding division facts, e.g.
- use their knowledge of tables and place value in calculations with multiples of 10 such as 30 × 7, 180 ÷ 3

Solving numerical problems / Algebra

A solve problems with or without a calculator
- solve two-step problems choosing appropriate operations
- deal with two constraints simultaneously
- interpret a calculator display of 4.5 as £4.50 in context of money
- carry out simple calculations involving negative numbers in context
B check the reasonableness of results with reference to the context or size of numbers
C begin to use simple formulae expressed in words
D use and interpret coordinates in the first quadrant

Written and calculator methods

A use efficient written methods of addition and subtraction and of short multiplication and division e.g.
- calculate 1202 + 45 + 367 or 1025 - 336
B add and subtract decimals to two places
C multiply a simple decimal by a single digit, e.g. calculate 36.2 × 8

Level 3 (L3)

Numbers & the number system

A understand place value in numbers to 1000, e.g.
- represent/compare numbers using number lines, 100-squares, base 10 materials, etc.
- recognise that some numbers can be represented as different arrays
- use understanding of place value to multiply/divide whole numbers by 10 (whole number answers)
B use place value to make approximations
C recognise negative numbers in contexts such as temperature
D recognise a wider range of sequences, e.g.
- recognise sequences of multiples of 2, 5 and 10

Fractions and decimals

A use simple fractions that are several parts of a whole and recognise when two simple fractions are equivalent, e.g.
- understand and use unit fractions such as 1/2, 1/4, 1/3, 1/5, 1/10 and find those fractions of shapes and sets of objects
- recognise and record fractions that are several parts of the whole such as 3/4, 2/5
- recognise some fractions that are equivalent to 1/2
B begin to use decimal notation in contexts such as money, e.g.
- order decimals with one dp, or two dp in context of money
- know that £3.06 equals 306p

Operations, relationships....

A derive associated division facts from known multiplication facts, e.g.
- given a number sentence, use understanding of operations to create related sentences, e.g. given 14 × 5 = 70, create 5 × 14 = 70, 70 ÷ 5 = 14, 70 ÷ 14 = 5, 14 × 5 = 10 × 5 add 4 × 5
- use inverses to find missing whole numbers in problems such as 'I think of a number, double it and add 5. The answer is 35. What was my number?'
B begin to understand the role of '=', the 'equals' sign, e.g.
- solve 'balancing' problems such as 7 × 10 = 82 - __

Mental methods

A add and subtract two-digit numbers mentally, e.g.
- calculate 36 + 19, 63 - 26, and complements to 100 such as 100 - 24
B use mental recall of the 2, 3, 4, 5 and 10 multiplication tables, e.g.
- multiply a two-digit number by 2, 3, 4 or 5
- understand finding a quarter of a number of objects as halving the number and halving again
- begin to know multiplication facts for ×6, ×8, ×9 and ×7 tables

Solving numerical problems

A use mental recall of addition and subtraction facts to 20 in solving problems involving larger numbers, e.g.
- choose to calculate mentally, on paper or with apparatus
- solve one-step whole number problems appropriately
- solve two-step problems that involve addition and subtraction
B solve whole number problems including those involving multiplication or division that may give rise to remainders, e.g.
- identify appropriate operations to use
- round up or down after simple division, depending on context

Written methods

A add and subtract threedigit numbers using written method, e.g.
- use written methods that involve bridging 10 or 100
- add and subtract decimals in the context of money, where bridging is not required
B multiply and divide two digit numbers by 2, 3, 4 or 5 as well as 10 with whole number answers and remainders, e.g.
- calculate 49 ÷ 3

Mathematics Attainment Target 3 (MA 3) Shape, Space and Measures

Level 5 (L5)

Properties of shape

A use a wider range of properties of 2-D and 3-D shapes, e.g.
- understand 'parallel' and begin to understand 'perpendicular' in relation to edges or faces
- classify quadrilaterals, including trapezium and kite, using their properties, e.g. number of parallel sides
- reason about special triangles and quadrilaterals, e.g. given the perimeter and one side of an isosceles triangle, find both possible triangles
- draw a parallelogram or trapezium of a given area on a square grid
- given the coordinates of three vertices of a parallelogram, find the fourth

B know and use the angle sum of a triangle and that of angles at a point, e.g.
- calculate 'missing angles' in triangles, including isosceles triangles or right-angled triangles, when only one/one other angle is given
- calculate angles on a straight line or at a point such as the angle between the hands of a clock, or intersecting diagonals at the centre of a regular hexagon

A identify all the symmetries of 2-D shapes (for rotation symmetry see Key Stage 3 programme of study)
- find lines of reflection symmetry in shapes and diagrams
- recognise order of rotation symmetry

B transform shapes
- reflect shapes in oblique (45°) mirror lines where the shape either does not touch the mirror line, or where the shape crosses the mirror line
- reflect shapes not presented on grids, by measuring perpendicular distances to/from the mirror
- reflect shapes in two mirror lines, where the shape is not parallel or perpendicular to either mirror
- rotate shapes, through 90° or 180°, when the centre of rotation is a vertex of the shape, and recognise such rotations
- translate shapes along an oblique line

C reason about shapes, positions and movements
- visualise a 3-D shape from its net and match vertices that will be joined
- visualise where patterns drawn on a 3-D shape will occur on its net, e.g. when shown a cube with patterns drawn on two or three faces, create the net to make the cube
- draw shapes with a fixed number of lines of symmetry

Measures

A measure and draw angles to the nearest degree, when constructing models and drawing or using shapes, e.g.
- measure and draw reflex angles to the nearest degree, when neither edge is horizontal/vertical
- construct a triangle given the length of two sides and the angle between them (accurate to 1 mm and 2°)

B use language associated with angle

C read and interpret scales on a range of measuring instruments, explaining what each labelled division represents

D solve problems involving the conversion of units, e.g.
- solve problems such as 1.5 kg ÷ 30g
- work out approximately how many km are equivalent to 20 miles

E make sensible estimates of a range of measures in relation to everyday situations

F understand and use the formula for the area of a rectangle and distinguish area from perimeter
- find the length of a rectangle given its perimeter and width
- find the area or perimeter of simple L shapes, given some edge lengths

Level 4 (L4)

Properties of shape

A use the properties of 2-D and 3-D shapes, e.g.
- recognise and name most quadrilaterals, e.g. trapezium, parallelogram, rhombus
- recognise right-angled, equilateral, isosceles and scalene triangles
- recognise an oblique line of symmetry in a shape
- use mathematical terms such as horizontal, vertical, congruent (same size, same shape)
- understand properties of shapes, e.g. why a square is a special rectangle
- visualise shapes and recognise them in different orientations

B make 3-D models by linking given faces or edges

Properties of position and movement

A draw common 2-D shapes in different orientations on grids, e.g.
- complete a rectangle which has two sides drawn at an oblique angle to the grid

B reflect simple shapes in a mirror line, e.g.
- use a grid to plot the reflection in a mirror line presented at 45° where the shape touches the line or not
- begin to use the distance of vertices from the mirror line to reflect shapes more accurately

C begin to rotate a simple shape or object about its centre or a vertex

D translate shapes horizontally or vertically

Measures

A choose and use appropriate units and instruments

B interpret, with appropriate accuracy, numbers on a range of measuring instruments, e.g.
- measure a length using mm, to within 2 mm
- measure and drawn acute and obtuse angles to the nearest 5°, when one edge is horizontal/vertical

C find perimeters of simple shapes and find areas by counting squares, e.g.
- use the terms 'area' and 'perimeter' accurately and consistently
- find areas by counting squares and part squares
- begin to find the area of shapes that need to be divided into rectangles
- use 'number of squares in a row times number of rows' to find the area of a rectangle

D use units of time, e.g.
- calculate time durations that go over the hour
- read and interpret timetables

Level 3 (L3)

Properties of shape

A classify 3-D and 2-D shapes in various ways using mathematical properties such as reflective symmetry for 2-D shapes, e.g.
- sort objects and shapes using more than one criterion, e.g. pentagon, not pentagon and all edges the same length/not the same length
- sort the shapes which have all edges the same length and all angles the same size from a set of mixed shapes and begin to understand the terms 'regular' and 'irregular'
- recognise right angles in shapes in different orientations
- recognise angles which are bigger/smaller than 90° and begin to know the terms 'obtuse' and 'acute'
- recognise right-angled and equilateral triangles
- demonstrate that a shape has reflection symmetry by folding and recognise when a shape does not have a line of symmetry
- recognise common 3-D shapes, e.g. triangular prism, square-based pyramid
- relate 3-D shapes to drawings and photographs of them, including from different viewpoints and begin to recognise nets of familiar 3-D shapes, e.g. cube, cuboid, triangular prism, square-based pyramid

Properties of position and movement

A recognise shapes in different orientations

B reflect shapes, presented on a grid, in a vertical or horizontal mirror line, e.g.
- reflect a shape even if the shape is at 45° to the mirror line, touching the line or not
- begin to reflect simple shapes in a mirror line presented at 45°

C describe position and movement, e.g.
- use terms such as left/right, clockwise/anticlockwise, quarter turn/90° to give directions along a route

Measures

A use non-standard units and standard metric units of length, capacity and mass in a range of contexts, e.g.
- measure a length to the nearest 1/2 cm
- read simple scales, e.g. increments of 2, 5 or 10

B use standard units of time, e.g.
- read a 12-hour clock and generally calculate time durations that do not go over the hour

C use a wider range of measures, e.g.
- begin to understand area as a measure of surface and perimeter as a measure of length
- begin to find areas of shapes by counting squares and explain answers as a number of squares even if not using standard units such as cm^2 or m^2
- recognise angles as a measure of turn and know that one whole turn is 360 degrees

Mathematics Attainment Target 4 (MA 4) Handling Data

Level 5 (L5)

Specifying the problem and planning, collecting data

A ask questions, plan how to answer them and collect the data required
B in probability, select methods based on equally likely outcomes and experimental evidence, as appropriate
- decide whether a probability can be calculated or whether it can only be estimated from the results of an experiment
C understand that different outcomes may result from repeating an experiment.

Processing and representing data

A understand and use the mean of discrete data, e.g.
- use the mean of a set of measurements from a science experiment
B understand and use the probability scale from 0 to 1 (from the Key Stage 3 programme of study)
C use methods based on equally likely outcomes and experimental evidence, as appropriate, to find and justify probabilities, and approximations to these (from the Key Stage 3 programme of study), e.g.
- compare two spinners, e.g. to find which is more likely to result in an even number
D create and interpret line graphs where the intermediate values have meaning, e.g.
- draw and use a conversion graph for pounds and euro

Interpreting data

A compare two simple distributions, using the range and one of mode, median or mean (mean and median are drawn from the Key Stage 3 programme of study)
- describe and compare two sets of football results, by using the range and mode
- solve problems such as 'Find five numbers where the mode is 6 and the range is 8'
B interpret graphs and diagrams, including pie charts, and draw conclusions
- interpret bar graphs with grouped data
- complete a two-way table, given some of the data
- interpret and compare pie charts where it is not necessary to measure angles
- read between labelled divisions on a scale, e.g. read 34 on a scale labelled in tens or 3.7 on a scale labelled in ones, and find differences to answer 'How much more…?'
- recognise the difference between discrete and continuous data
- recognise when information is presented in a misleading way, e.g. compare two pie charts where the sample sizes are different
- when drawing conclusions, identify further questions to ask
- describe and predict outcomes from data using the language of chance or likelihood

Level 4 (L4)

Processing and representing data

A collect discrete data, e.g.
- given a problem, suggest possible answers and data to collect
- test a hypothesis about the frequency of an event by collecting data, e.g. collect dice scores to test ideas about how many scores of 6 will occur during 50 throws of a dice
B group data, where appropriate, in equal class intervals, e.g.
- decide on a suitable class interval when collecting or representing data about pupils' hours per week spent watching TV
C record discrete data using a frequency table
D represent collected data in frequency diagrams, e.g.
- suggest an appropriate frequency diagram to represent particular data, e.g. decide whether a bar chart, Venn diagram or pictogram would be most appropriate and for pictograms use one symbol to represent, say, 2, 5, 10 or 100
E construct simple line graphs
- decide upon an appropriate scale for a graph, e.g. labelled divisions representing 2, 5, 10, 100
F continue to use Venn and Carroll diagrams to record their sorting and classifying of information, e.g.
- represent sorting using two criteria typical of level 3 and 4 mathematics such as sorting numbers using properties 'multiples of 8' and 'multiples of 6'

Interpreting data

A understand and use the mode and range to describe sets of data
- use mode and range to describe data relating to shoe sizes in their class and begin to compare their data with data from another class
B interpret frequency diagrams and simple line graphs
- interpret simple pie charts
- interpret the scale on bar graphs and line graphs, reading between the labelled divisions, e.g. reading 17 on a scale labelled in fives
- interpret the total amount of data represented
- compare data sets and respond to questions, e.g. 'How does our data about favourite TV programmes compare to the data from Year 3 children?'
- in the context of data relating to everyday situations, understand the language of probability such as 'more likely, likely, equally likely, fair, unfair, certain'

Level 3 (L3)

Processing and representing data

A gather information, e.g.
- decide what data to collect to answer a question, e.g. what is the most common way to travel to school
- make appropriate choices for recording data, e.g. a tally chart or frequency table
B construct bar charts and pictograms, where the symbol represents a group of units, e.g.
- decide how best to represent data, e.g. whether a bar chart, Venn diagram or pictogram would show the information most clearly
- decide upon an appropriate scale for a graph, e.g. labelled divisions of 2, or, for a pictogram, one symbol to represent 2 or 5
C use Venn and Carroll diagrams to record their sorting and classifying of information, e.g.
- represent sorting using one or two criteria typical of level 2 and 3 mathematics, e.g. shapes sorted using properties such as right angles and equal sides

Interpreting data

A extract and interpret information presented in simple tables, lists, bar charts and pictograms, e.g.
- use a key to interpret represented data
- read scales labelled in twos, fives and tens, including reading between labelled divisions such as a point halfway between 40 and 50 or 8 and 10
- compare data, e.g. say how many more… than… and recognise the category that has most/least
- respond to questions of a more complex nature such as 'How many children took part in this survey altogether?' or 'How would the data differ if we asked the children in Year 6?'
- in the context of data relating to everyday situations, understand the idea of 'certain' and 'impossible' relating to probability

Assessing Pupil Progress in Mathematics (APP)
and Identifying Gaps in Pupil's Learning (Year 5 - Level 3)

Name		Date	

This test can be used to confirm a teacher's informal assessment of a pupil. It can also be used to indicate gaps in a pupil's learning.

How to confirm a teacher's informal assessment of a pupil

The test is in two parts. One part consists of an un-timed written paper test for the pupil to complete unaided. The other part (found below) consists of a simple grid for the teacher to complete after observing the pupil in a normal classroom situation. This part of the assessment indicates performance mainly against Attainment Target 1 – Using and Applying Mathematics. The scores for the two tests should be added together and a National Curriculum sub-level awarded using the information in the table at the bottom of this page. The resulting score should give a clear indication of which sub-level the pupil is working at within the levels found in the English National Curriculum.

How to indicate gaps in a pupil's learning

Each question on the written paper is accompanied by the learning objective it represents taken from the tables reproduced at the beginning of the book. By referring to the incorrect questions a list of learning objectives which indicate the gaps in the pupil's learning can quickly and easily be made up.

Teacher Assessment of Attainment Target 1 – Using & Applying (Ma1) and some of Attainment Target 4 – Handling and Data (Ma4) 1 mark indicates some ability	Mark 0 or 1 for each statement
Ma1/L3 – Problem solving - Part A Select the mathematics they use in a wider	
Ma1/L3 – Problem solving - Part B Try different approaches of overcoming	
Ma1/L3 – Problem solving - Part B Find ways of overcoming difficulties that arise	
Ma1/L3 – Communicating - Part A Begin to organise their work and check results	
Ma1/L3 – Communicating - Part B Discuss their mathematical work and begin to	
Ma1/L3 – Communicating - Part C Use and interpret mathematical symbols and	
Ma1/L3 – Reasoning - Part A Understand a general statement by finding	
Ma1/L3 – Reasoning - Part B Review their work and reasoning	
Ma 4/L3 – Processing and representing data - Part A Gather information	
Ma 4/L3 – Processing and representing data – Part B Construct bar charts and	
Total =	

Teacher Assessment of AT1 from above.		10
Paper Test Score		40
Total		50
Sub Level Awarded		

Level 3a high = 42 - 50

Level 3b secure = 32 - 41

Level 3c low = 21 - 31

Below Level 3 = 20 or less

1. Put these numbers in order, smallest first.

149   181   180   184   418

[ ] [ ] [ ] [ ] [ ]

Ma2/L3
Numbers and the
number system
Part A

*Understand place
values in numbers to
1000*

1 mark [ ]

2. Tick, in each box, which of the two numbers is nearest to 5.

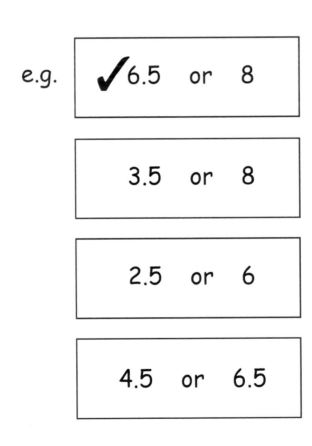

e.g. | ✓6.5   or   8 |

| 3.5   or   8 |

| 2.5   or   6 |

| 4.5   or   6.5 |

Ma2/L3
Numbers and the
number system
Part B

*Use place value to
make approximations*

1 mark [ ]

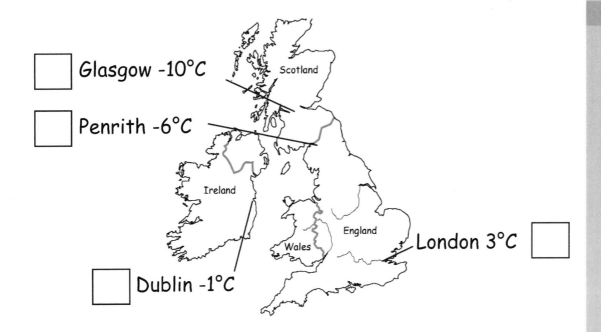

☐ Glasgow -10°C

☐ Penrith -6°C

London 3°C ☐

☐ Dublin -1°C

3a. Tick the coldest place on the map.

3b. What is the difference in temperature
     between London and Glasgow?

     ┌─────────────┐
     │   °C   │
     └─────────────┘

Ma2/L3
Numbers and the
number system
Part C

*Recognise negative
numbers in contexts
such as temperature*

3 marks ☐

☐

☐

3c. If the temperature in Glasgow increases by
     7 degrees Celsius, what would the new
     temperature be?

     ┌─────────────┐
     │   °C   │
     └─────────────┘

4. Write in the missing numbers.

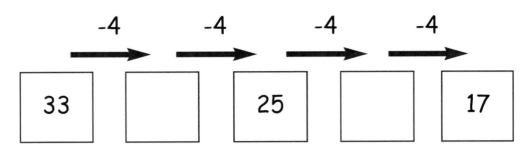

Teacher's notes

Ma2/L3
Numbers and the
number system
Part D

*Recognise a wider
range of sequences*

1 mark

5. Write in the next number in the sequence.

| 25 | 30 | 35 | | |

Ma2/L3
Numbers and the
number system
Part D

*Recognise a wider
range of sequences*

1 mark

6. Place $\frac{1}{2}$, and $\frac{1}{4}$ on this number line.

0   1

Ma2/L3
Fractions and
decimals
Part A

*Use simple fractions
that are several parts
of a whole and
recognise when two
simple fractions are
equivalent*

1 mark

7. Circle the fractions that are equal to $\frac{1}{2}$?

$$\frac{2}{4} \qquad \frac{8}{4} \qquad \frac{10}{20} \qquad \frac{3}{9}$$

Ma2/L3
Fractions and
decimals
Part A

*Use simple fractions
that are several parts
of a whole and
recognise when two
simple fractions are
equivalent*

1 mark

8. Hannah buys 4 new pens. Each pen costs £1.30. How much does she pay altogether?

£ [ ]

Ma2/L3
Fractions and decimals
Part B

Begin to use decimal notation in contexts such as money

1 mark [ ]

9. How much money is here?
£5, £10, £2, £1, 20p, 20p, 10p

£ [ ]

Ma2/L3
Fractions and decimals
Part B

Begin to use decimal notation in contexts such as money

1 mark [ ]

10. 7 × 8 = 56

so 56 ÷ 7 = [ ]

and 56 ÷ 8 = [ ]

Ma2/L3
Operations, relationships between them
Part A

Derive associated division facts from known multiplication facts

1 mark [ ]

11.

9 + 7 = 2 + [ ]

Ma2/L3
Operations, relationships between them
Part B

Begin to understand the role of '=', the 'equals' sign

1 mark [ ]

12.

$42 + 56 =$ ⬜

Teacher's notes

Ma2/L3
Mental Methods
Part A

Add and Subtract two-digit numbers mentally

1 mark ⬜

13.

$60 - 44 =$ ⬜

Ma2/L3
Mental Methods
Part A

Add and subtract two-digit numbers mentally

1 mark ⬜

14.

⬜ × ⬜ $= 35$

⬜ × ⬜ $= 16$

Ma2/L3
Mental Methods
Part B

Use mental recall of the 2, 3, 4, 5 and 10 multiplication tables

1 mark ⬜

15. If 5 apples cost 80p, how much would 15 apples cost?

£ ⬜

Ma2/L3
Mental Methods
Part B

Use mental recall of the 2, 3, 4, 5 and 10 multiplication tables

1 mark ⬜

16. Josh has 90p. He buys an apple for 20p and a banana for 40p. How much does he have left?

p ⬜

Ma2/L3
Solving numerical problems
Part A

Use mental recall of addition and subtraction facts to 20 in solving problems involving larger numbers

1 mark ⬜

17. Look at the table below. There are 56 children in the hall that are either 8, 9 or 10 years old. How many children are 10 years old?

Age	Number of Children
Age 8	10
Age 9	23
Age 10	

Teacher's notes

Ma2/L3
Solving numerical problems
Part B

Solve whole number problems including those involving multiplication or division that may give rise to remainders

1 mark

18. Pens are sold in packs of 8. How many pens are there in 3 packs?

pens

Ma2/L3
Solving numerical problems
Part B

Solve whole number problems including those involving multiplication or division that may give rise to remainders

1 mark

19.

536 + 343 =

Ma2/L3
Written Methods
Part A

Add and subtract three digit numbers using written method

1 mark

20.

$343 - 170 =$ ☐

21.

What is $14 \times 5 =$ ☐

22. Tick the divisions that have an answer of 4.

$20 \div 10 =$

$20 \div 5 =$

$20 \div 4 =$

$8 \div 2 =$

23. Tick the divisions that have a remainder of 1.

$29 \div 4 =$

$12 \div 4 =$

$22 \div 4 =$

$17 \div 4 =$

Teacher's notes

Ma2/L3
Written methods
Part A

Add and subtract three-digit numbers using written method

1 mark

Ma2/L3
Written methods
Part B

Multiply and divide two-digit numbers by 2, 3, 4 and 5 as well as 10 with whole number answers and remainders

1 mark

Ma2/L3
Written methods
Part B

Multiply and divide two-digit numbers by 2, 3, 4 and 5 as well as 10 with whole number answers and remainders

1 mark

Ma2/L3
Written methods
Part B

Multiply and divide two-digit numbers by 2, 3, 4 and 5 as well as 10 with whole number answers and remainders

1 mark

24. Write the number of right-angles inside each shape.

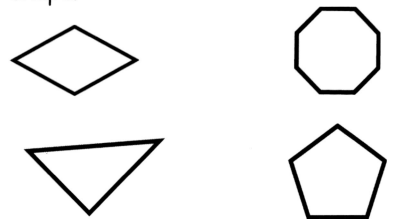

25a. Put a tick in the right-angle triangle.

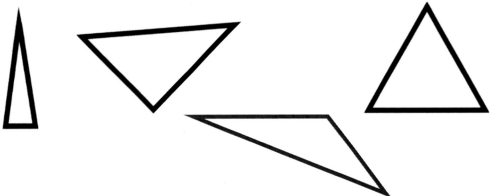

25b. Put a circle around the equilateral triangle.

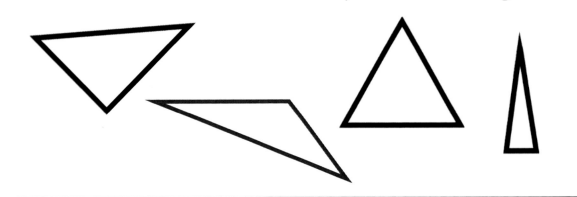

26. Tick the cuboid.

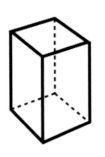   

27. Tick the two nets that will make a cube.

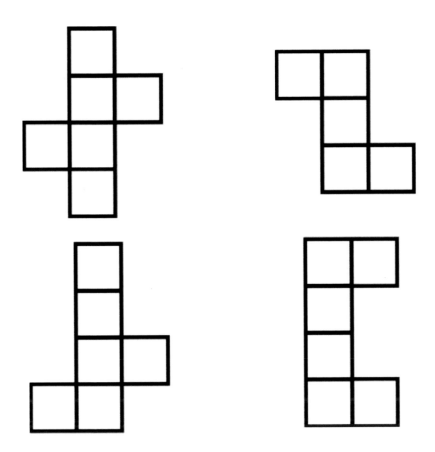

Teacher's notes

Ma3/L3
Properties of Shape
Part B

Begin to recognise nets of familiar 3-D shapes

1 mark

---

28. What is the name of this shape?

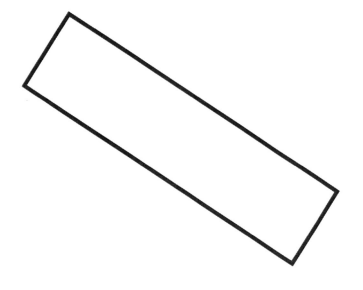

It is a...

29. Reflect the coloured shapes in the mirror line.

30. Tick the correct word.

start    finish

Has this frog been rotated clockwise or anticlockwise?

clockwise ☐   anticlockwise ☐

31. How long is this line?

cm

_____

Teacher's notes

Ma3/L3
Measures
Part A

Use non-standard units and standard metric units of length, capacity and mass in a range of contexts

1 mark

32. How long is a lesson that starts at 9.10am and finishes at 9.35am?

minutes

Ma3/L3
Measures
Part B

Use standard units of time

1 mark

33. How many degrees make a whole turn?

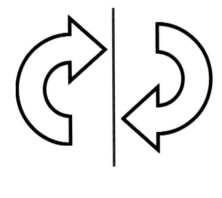

o

Ma3/L3
Measures
Part C

Use a wider range of measures

1 mark

34. Copy these two shapes onto the Carroll diagram below.

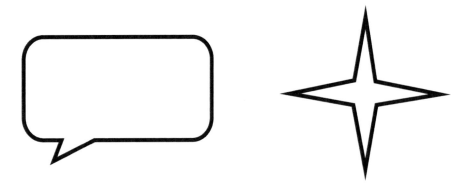

	Right Angles	No Right Angles
A line of symmetry		
No line of symmetry		

Teacher's notes

Ma4/L3
Processing and representing data
Parts A and B

(See Teacher Assessment on the first page of this test paper.)

Ma4/L3
Processing and representing data
Part C

Use Venn and Carroll diagrams to record their sorting and classifying of information

1 mark

A graph to show how children in class 1 travel to school

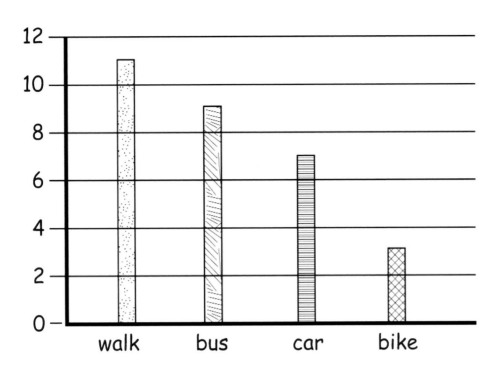

35. How many children in class 1 travel
    to school by car?

    | |
    | children |

Ma4/L3
Interpreting data
Part A

*Extract and interpret
information presented
in simple tables, lists,
bar charts and
pictograms*

36. How many more children travel by
    bus than bike?

    | |
    | children |

3 marks

37. How many children took part in this survey?

    | |
    | children |

19

Assessing Pupil Progress in Mathematics (APP)
and Identifying Gaps in Pupil's Learning (Year 5 - Level 4)

Name [ ]   Date [ ]

This test can be used to confirm a teacher's informal assessment of a pupil. It can also be used to indicate gaps in a pupil's learning.

How to confirm a teacher's informal assessment of a pupil
The test is in two parts. One part consists of an un-timed written paper test for the pupil to complete unaided. The other part (found below) consists of a simple grid for the teacher to complete after observing the pupil in a normal classroom situation. This part of the assessment indicates performance mainly against Attainment Target 1 – Using and Applying Mathematics. The scores for the two tests should be added together and a National Curriculum sub-level awarded using the information in the table at the bottom of this page. The resulting score should give a clear indication of which sub-level the pupil is working at within the levels found in the English National Curriculum.

How to indicate gaps in a pupil's learning
Each question on the written paper is accompanied by the learning objective it represents taken from the tables reproduced at the beginning of the book. By referring to the incorrect questions a list of learning objectives which indicate the gaps in the pupil's learning can quickly and easily be made up.

Teacher Assessment of Attainment Target 1 – Using & Applying (Ma1) and some of Attainment Target 4 – Handling and Data (Ma4) 2 marks indicates competent 1 mark indicates some ability 0 mark indicates unable to carry out	Mark 0, 1 or 2 for each statement
Ma1/L4 – Problem solving – Part A Develop own strategies for solving problems	
Ma1/L4 – Problem solving – Part B Use their own strategies within mathematics and in applying mathematics to practical context	
Ma1/L4 – Communicating – Part A Show understanding of situations by describing them mathematically using symbols, words and diagrams.	
Ma1/L4 – Reasoning – Part A Search for a solution by trying out ideas of their own	
Ma4/L4 - Processing and representing data - Parts A – D Collect, group, record and represent discrete data.	
Total =	

Teacher Assessment of AT1 from above.		10
Paper Test Score		40
Total		50
Sub Level Awarded		

Level 4a high	= 42 - 50
Level 4b secure	= 32 - 41
Level 4c low	= 21 - 31
Below Level 4	= 20 or less

1. Fill in the missing numbers in this sequence.

| | 2.6 | 2.7 | | | 3.0 | |

Teacher's notes

Ma2/L4
Numbers and the number system
Part A

Recognise and describe number patterns

1 mark

2. Tick the boxes that are square numbers.

| 25 | 23 | 4 | 36 | 58 |

Ma2/L4
Numbers and the number system
Part B

Recognise and describe number relationships including multiple, factor and square

1 mark

3.

22 x 10 =

239 x 100 =

2320 ÷ 10 =

3500 ÷ 100 =

Ma2/L4
Numbers and the number system
Part C

Use place value to multiply and divide whole numbers by 10 or 100

1 mark

4. If Gerry wants to eat $\frac{1}{6}$ of this chocolate bar. How many pieces will be left?

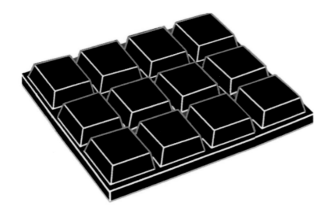

pieces

Ma2/L4
Fractions, decimals, percentages and ratio
Part A

Recognise approximate proportions of a whole and use simple fractions and percentages to describe these

1 mark

5. Put these numbers in order, smallest first.

| 2.5 | 1.43 | 1.191 |

| | | |

Ma2/L4
Fractions, decimals, percentages and ratio
Part B

Order decimals to three decimal places

1 mark

6. The ratio of boys to girls is 3:1. If there are 9 boys, how many girls are there?

girls

Ma2/L4
Fractions, decimals, percentages and ratio
Part C

Begin to understand simple ratio

1 mark

7. I am thinking of a number.
I multiply it by 4,
I take away 2,
The answer is 6.
What number am I thinking of?

Ma2/L4
Operations, relationships between them
Part A

Use inverse operations

1 mark

8.

$$900 = 150 \times \boxed{}$$

Ma2/L4
Operations, relationships between them
Part A

Use inverse operations

1 mark

9.

$$\boxed{} - 200 = 380$$

Ma2/L4
Operations, relationships between them
Part A

Use inverse operations

1 mark

© Topical Resources. May be photocopied for classroom use only.

10. Write a number in the box to make the sum balance.

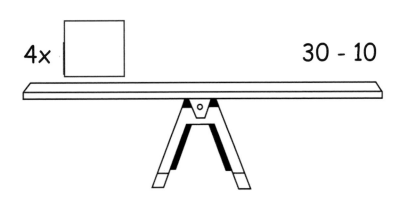

4x [ ]   30 - 10

Teacher's notes

Ma2/L4
Operations,
relationships
between them
Part A

*Use inverse
operations*

1 mark

11.

$17 - (3 \times 2) =$ [ ]

Ma2/L4
Operations,
relationships
between them
Part B

*Understand the use of
brackets in simple
calculations*

1 mark [ ]

12.

$56 \div 7 =$ [ ]

Ma2/L4
Operations,
relationships
between them
Part C

*Quickly derive division
facts that correspond
to multiplication facts
up to 10 x 10*

1 mark

13.

$1999 + 18 =$ [ ]

Ma2/L4
Mental methods
Part A

*Use a range of mental
methods of
computation with the
four operations*

1 mark

14.

4 x 8 =	3 x 6 =	3 x 7 =
32 ÷ 4 =	18 ÷ 3 =	21 ÷ 7 =
3 x 8 =	6 x 6 =	7 x 8 =
24 ÷ 3 =	42 ÷ 7 =	56 ÷ 8 =

15. There are 23 children in Mrs. Higham's class.
There is one more boy than girl.
How many girls are there in the class?

girls

16. Gary buys 3 pens at 99p.
How much do they cost?

£

17. In the Westhall family, to find the amount of pocket money...

Multiply their age by 10p, then add 20p.

How much will an 8 year old get?

p

18.

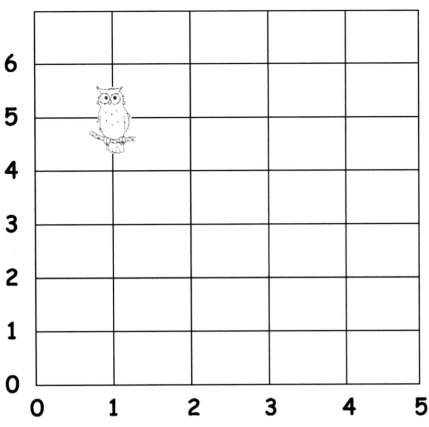

What are the co-ordinates of the owl?

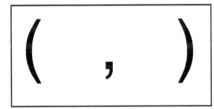

Ma2/L4
Solving numerical problems
Part D

Use and interpret co-ordinates in the 1st quadrant

1 mark

19.

500 – 148 =

Ma2/L4
Written and calculator methods
Part A

Use efficient written methods of addition, subtraction and of short multiplication and division

1 mark

20.

56 × 42 =

Ma2/L4
Written and calculator methods
Part A

Use efficient written methods of addition, subtraction and of short multiplication and division

1 mark

21.

$$237 \div 3 =$$ ☐

22.

$$1.6 + 3.5 =$$ ☐

23.

$$12.6 + 4.31 =$$ ☐

24.

$$4.7 - 2.9 =$$ ☐

25.

$$2.5 \times 3 =$$ ☐

26. Draw in any lines of symmetry on these shapes:

Ma3/L4
Properties of shape
Part A

Use the properties of 2-D and 3-D shapes

1 mark

27. Add these two shapes to the net below to make a net for a cuboid.

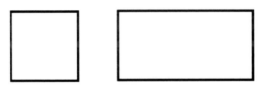

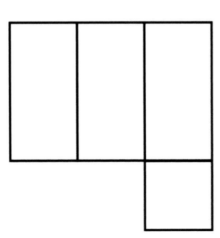

Ma3/L4
Properties of shape
Part B

Make 3-D models by linking given faces or edges

1 mark

28. Draw 2 more lines to make a rectangle.

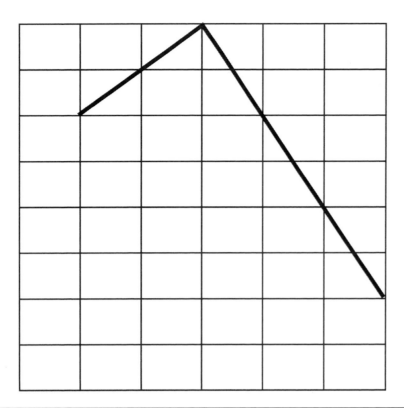

Teacher's notes

Ma3/L4
Properties of position and movement
Part A

Draw common 2-D shapes in different orientations on grids

1 mark

29. Draw in 2 lines of symmetry.

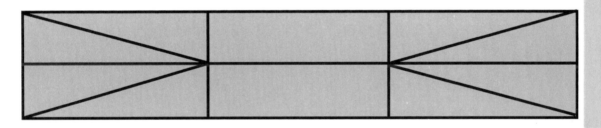

Ma3/L4
Properties of position and movement
Part B

Reflect simple shapes in a mirror line

1 mark

30. Rotate this shape one half turn about its centre 'c' and draw the new shape.

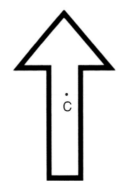

Ma3/L4
Properties of position and movement
Part C

Begin to rotate a simple shape or object about its centre or a vertex

1 mark

31. Translate this shape 4 squares to the right.

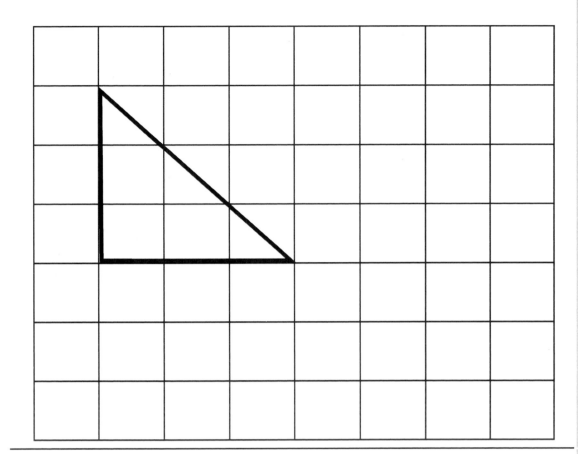

Teacher's notes

Ma3/L4
Properties of position and movement
Part D

Translate shapes horizontally or vertically

1 mark

32. What units would you use to measure the following? Show your answer with arrows.

The amount of water in a glass

The length of a pencil

The amount of water in a bath

| centimetres |

| millilitres |

| litres |

Ma3/L4
Measures
Part A

Choose and use appropriate units and instruments

1 mark

33. Mark the number 47kg on this scale.

Teacher's notes

Ma3/L4
Measures
Part B

Interpret, with appropriate accuracy, numbers on a range of measuring instruments

1 mark

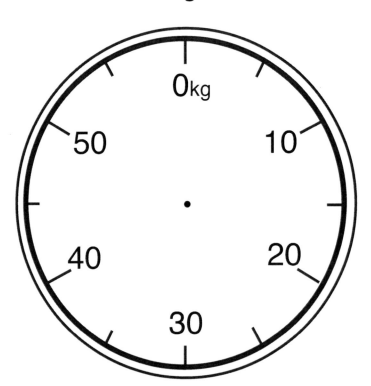

34. Find the area and perimeter of this shape.
   Each square is 1cm²

Ma3/L4
Measures
Part C

Find the perimeters of simple shapes and find areas by counting squares

1 mark

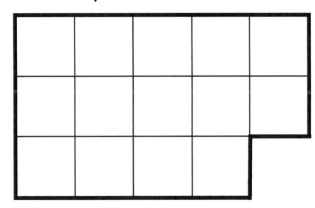

Area =   cm²   Perimeter =   cm

35. A television programme begins at 2.45pm and finishes at 3.30pm.
   How long was the programme?

Ma3/L4
Measures
Part D

Use units of time

1 mark

        minutes

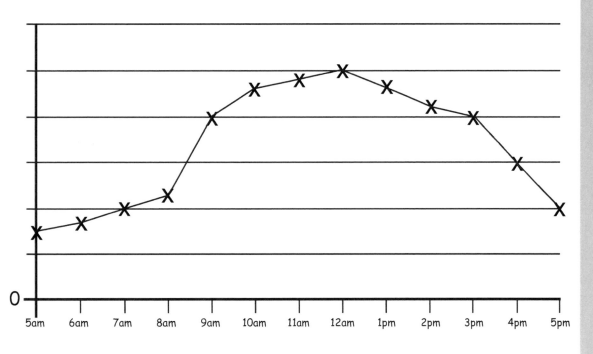

36. If the temperature was 10°C at 7am, label the scale on the y axis that starts from 0.

37. For how many hours was the temperature above 20°C?

hours

Ma4/L4
Interpreting data
Part B

(note – this statement is slightly out of order)

Interpret frequency diagrams and simple line graphs

1 mark

38 How many children are in class 1?

	Class 1	Class 2
8 years old	13	19
Not 8 years old	15	12

children

Teacher's notes

Ma4/L4
Processing and
representing data
Part F

Continue to use Venr
and Carroll diagrams
to record their sorting
and classifying of
information

1 mark ☐

39. These are the test scores of 7 children.

16   14   15   15   18   15   20

What is the mode? ☐

What is the range? ☐

Ma4/L4
Interpreting data
Part A

Understand and use
the mode and range
describe sets of data

2 marks ☐

☐

Assessing Pupil Progress in Mathematics (APP)
and Identifying Gaps in Pupil's Learning (Year 5 - Level 5)

Name		Date	

This test can be used to confirm a teacher's informal assessment of a pupil. It can also be used to indicate gaps in a pupil's learning.

How to confirm a teacher's informal assessment of a pupil

The test is in two parts. One part consists of an un-timed written paper test for the pupil to complete unaided. The other part (found below) consists of a simple grid for the teacher to complete after observing the pupil in a normal classroom situation. This part of the assessment indicates performance mainly against Attainment Target 1 – Using and Applying Mathematics. The scores for the two tests should be added together and a National Curriculum sub-level awarded using the information in the table at the bottom of this page. The resulting score should give a clear indication of which sub-level the pupil is working at within the levels found in the English National Curriculum.

How to indicate gaps in a pupil's learning.

Each question on the written paper is accompanied by the learning objective it represents taken from the tables reproduced at the beginning of the book. By referring to the incorrect questions a list of learning objectives which indicate the gaps in the pupil's learning can quickly and easily be made up.

Teacher Assessment of Attainment Target 1 – Using & Applying (Ma1) and some of Attainment Target 4 – Handling and Data (Ma4) 1 mark indicates some ability 0 mark indicates unable to carry out	Mark 0 or 1 for each statement
Ma1/L5 – **Problem solving – Part A** Identify and obtain necessary information to carry through a task and solve mathematical problems	
Ma1/L5 – **Problem solving – Part B** Check results, checking whether they are reasonable	
Ma1/L5 – **Problem solving – Part C** Solve word problems and investigations from a range of contexts	
Ma1/L5 – **Communicating – Part A** Present information and results in a clear and organised way	
Ma1/L5 – **Reasoning – Part A** Draw simple conclusions of their own and give an explanation of their reasoning	
Ma3/L5 – **Measures - Part E** Make sensible estimates of a range of measure in relation to everyday	
Ma4/ L5 – **Specifying the problem and planning, collecting data – Part A** Ask questions, plan how to answer them and collect the data required	
Ma4/L5 – **Specifying the problem and planning, collecting data – Part B** In probability, select methods based on equally likely outcomes and experimental evidence as appropriate	
Ma4/L5 – **Specifying the problem and planning, collecting data – Part C** Understand that different outcomes may result from repeating an experiment	
Ma 4/L5 – **Interpreting data – Part A -** Compare two simple distributions, using the range and one of mode, median or mean	
Total =	

	Actual	Possible
Teacher Assessment of AT1 from above.		10
Paper Test Score		40
Total		50
Sub Level Awarded		

Level 5a high = 42 - 50

Level 5b secure = 32 - 41

Level 5c low = 21 - 31

Below Level 5 = 20 or less

1.

$22.1 \times 10 =$ [ ] $239.2 \times 100 =$ [ ]

$232 \div 10 =$ [ ] $351 \div 100 =$ [ ]

2. 6.2 to the nearest whole number = [ ]

16.5 to the nearest whole number = [ ]

3. Order these places in the box from coldest to hottest.

Paris 16°C

London 6°C

Madrid 24°C

Dublin -6°C

Glasgow -10°C

Oslo -27°C

Coldest
1 _____
2 _____
3 _____
4 _____
5 _____
6 _____
Hottest

Teacher's notes

Ma2/L5
Numbers and the number system
Part A

Use understanding o place value to multip. and divide whole numbers and decim. by 10,100 and 1000 and explain the effec

1 mark [ ]

Ma2/L5
Numbers and the number system
Part B

Round decimals to th nearest decimal plac

2 marks [ ]

[ ]

Ma2/L5
Numbers and the number system
Part C

Order negative numbers in context

1 mark [ ]

4.   Tick the prime numbers.

| 77 | 23 | 39 | 19 |

Teacher's notes

Ma2/L5
Numbers and the number system
Part D

Recognise and describe number patterns and relationships

1 mark

5.   Look at this sequence...

| 4 | 9 | 14 | 19 |

.   Will 47 be in this sequence? Circle Yes or No.

Explain why _____

_____

_____

Ma2/L5
Numbers and the number system
Part D

Recognise and describe number patterns and relationships

1 mark

6. Match the fractions and decimals to their percentages.

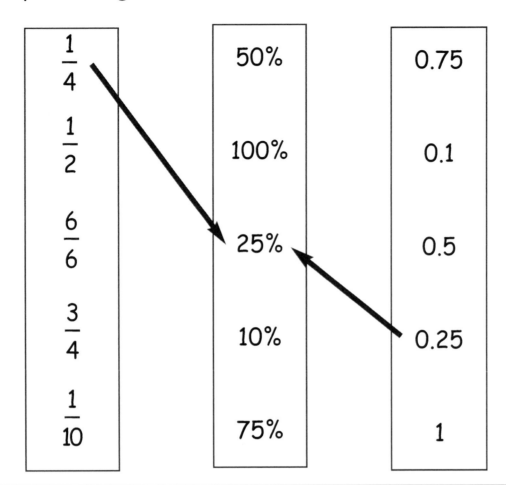

Teacher's notes

Ma2/L5
Fractions, decimals, percentages, ratios and proportion
Part A

Use equivalence between fractions

1 mark ☐

7. Reduce these fractions to their simplest form.

$$\frac{10}{40} =$$

$$\frac{2}{12} =$$

$$\frac{3}{6} =$$

$$\frac{6}{8} =$$

$$\frac{6}{18} =$$

Ma2/L5
Fractions, decimals, percentages, ratios and proportion
Part B

Reduce a fraction to its simplest form by cancelling common factors

1 mark ☐

8. Put these fractions in order, smallest first.

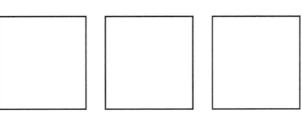

Ma2/L5
Fractions, decimals,
percentages, ratios
and proportion
Part C

*Order fractions and
decimals*

1 mark

---

9. This is a recipe for 8 people...

100g sugar

200g flour

4 eggs

100ml of milk

If the recipe was for 12 people - how much flour would you need?

| g |

Ma2/L5
Fractions, decimals,
percentages, ratios
and proportion
Part D

*Understand simple
ratio*

1 mark

10

$\frac{2}{3}$ of 75 =

15% of 60 =

Ma2/L5
Operations,
relationships
between them
Part A

*Use known facts,
place value and
knowledge of
operations to calculate*

1 mark

11.

$$\boxed{} \times \boxed{} = \boxed{2\,|\,4\,|\,0\,|\,0}$$

Ma2/L5
Operations, relationships between them
Part B

Apply inverse operations

1 mark ☐

12.

$$(49 \div 7) \times 8 = \boxed{}$$

Ma2/L5
Operations, relationships between them
Part C

Use brackets appropriately

1 mark ☐

13. Inside an aeroplane it is 16°C.
Outside it is -45°C.
What is the difference in temperature?

$$\boxed{}\ ^{\circ}C$$

Ma2/L5
Mental, written and calculator methods
Part A

Add and subtract negative numbers in context

1 mark ☐

14. Use estimation to find the approximate value:

199 x 49 is approximately $\boxed{}$

Ma2/L5
Mental, written and calculator methods
Part B

Estimate using approximations

1 mark ☐

15. If a wall is 12.53m long and I extend it by 1.34m – what is its new length?

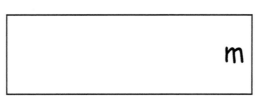

m

16. Use a Calculator for this question only to find the following amount:

15% of 150ml =

ml

17.

608 ÷ 16 =

329 x 82 =

18. In Moscow the temperature is –25°C
    The temperature drops 15°C.
    What is the temperature now?

    | °C |

Teacher's notes

Ma2/L5
Solving numerical
problems
Part A

*Solve simple problem
involving ordering,
adding and
subtracting negative
numbers in context*

1 mark

19. The ratio of boys to girls is 7:3.
    If there are 18 girls, how many boys are
    there?

    | boys |

Ma2/L5
Solving numerical
problems
Part B

*Solve simple problem
involving ratio and
direct proportion*

1 mark

20. There are 1999 children in a large secondary
    school. How many children would there be in 5
    schools of this size?

    | children |

Ma2/L5
Solving numerical
problems
Part C

*Approximate to chec
answers to problems
are of the correct
magnitude*

1 mark

21. Carolyn says: 249 x 107 = 2643
    Use approximation to show that she **must be
    incorrect**.

Ma2/L5
Solving numerical
problems
Part D

*Check solutions by
applying inverse
operations or
estimating using
approximations*

1 mark

22.

If $2x + 7 = 17$ $x =$

23.

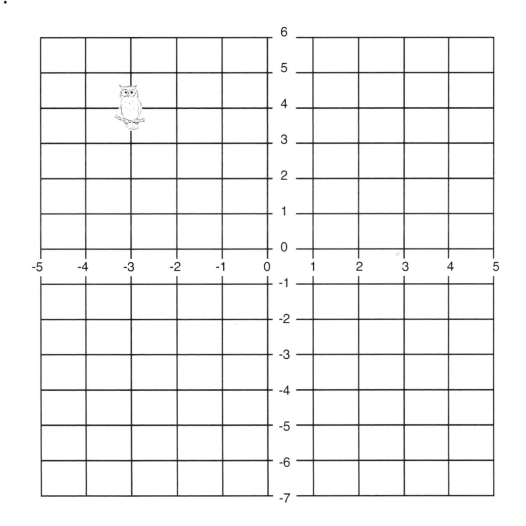

What are the co-ordinates of the owl?

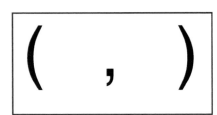

24. Tick the shapes that have exactly two sets of parallel lines.

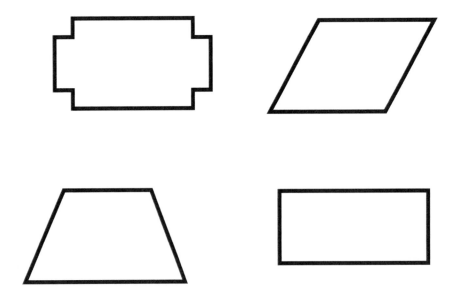

Teacher's notes

Ma3/L5
Properties of shape
Part A

Use a wider range o
2-D and 3-D shapes

1 mark

25. Without using a protractor, calculate how many degrees the missing angle is.

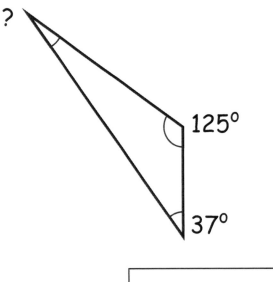

? =   °

Ma3/L5
Properties of Shape
Part B

Know and use the
angle sum of a
triangle and that of
angles at a point

1 mark

© **Topical Resources.** May be photocopied for classroom use only.

26. Here is a shape. Tick the translation. Put a star on the reflection.

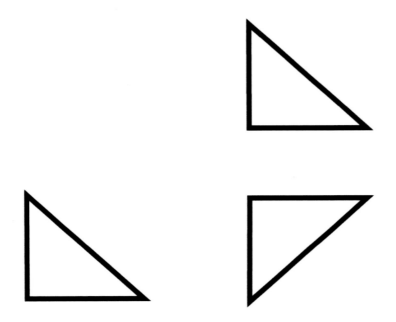

Teacher's notes

Ma3/L5
Properties of position and movement
Part A

Identify all the symmetries of 2-D shapes

1 mark

27. Reflect this shape in the mirror line.

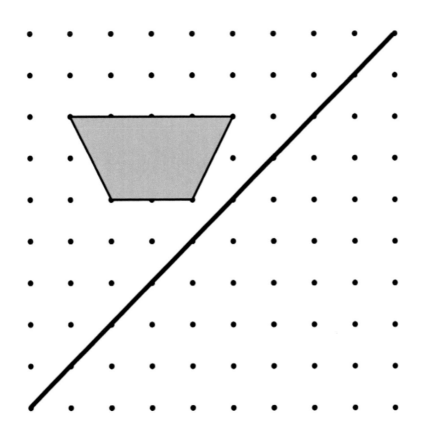

Ma3/L5
Properties of position and movement
Part B

Transform shapes

1 mark

28. On this grid, draw a pentagon with exactly one line of symmetry - use the line that has already been drawn for you.

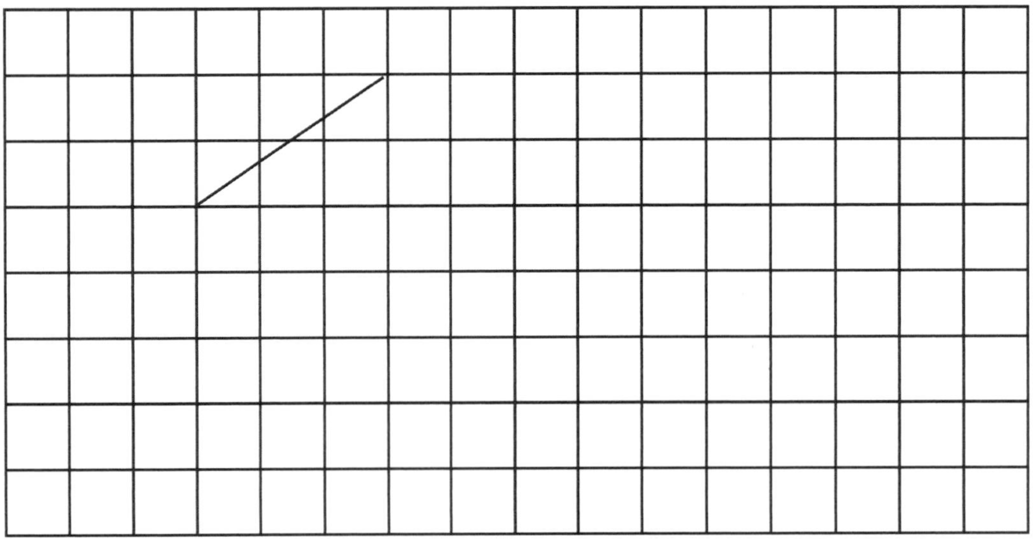

29. With a protractor, use the line to make a triangle with angles of 90°, 27° and 63°.

30. Count the types of angle in the triangle you have drawn:

Number of reflex angles =

Number of obtuse angles =

Number of right angles =

Number of acute angles =

31. How many millilitres will I need to add to this jug to make a litre of water?

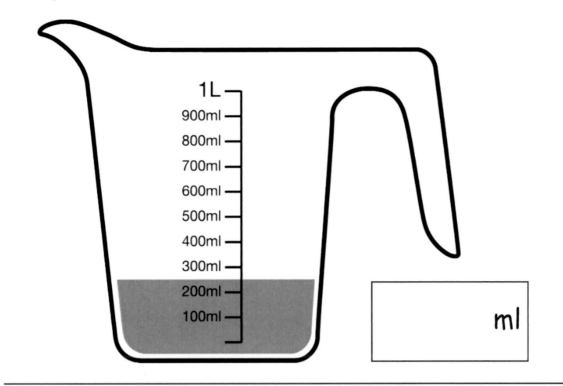

ml

Ma3/L5
Measures
Part C

Read and interpret scales on a range of measuring instruments, explaining what each labelled division represents

1 mark ☐

32. Andrew runs 4 kilometres and 400 centimetres. How far is this in metres?

metres

Ma3/L5
Measures
Part D

Solve problems involving the conversion of units

1 mark ☐

(For Part E see page 33)

33. The area of a rectangle is 24cm². If one side is 4cm long...

How long is the other side? | cm |

What is the perimeter of the shape? | cm |

Ma3/L5
Measures
Part F

Understand and use the formula for the area of a rectangle and distinguish area from perimeter

1 mark ☐

34. These are the test scores that 5 children scored...

| 10 | 5 | 5 | 7 | 8 |

What is the mean?

Teacher's notes

Ma4/L5
Processing and representing data
Part A

Understand and use the mean of discrete data

1 mark

---

35. If I roll a die, mark on the line with an arrow the probability of scoring less than 6?

0   1

Ma4/L5
Processing and representing data
Part B

Understand and use the probability scale from 0-1

1 mark

---

36. Match the event to the probability. The following letters are in a bag... A, B, B, B, C, D

Picking a letter B

Picking a letter E

Picking a letter in the 1st half of the alphabet

Picking out a letter C

Picking out a letter A

Certain

Likely

Evens

Unlikely

Impossible

Ma4/L5
Processing and representing data
Part C

Use methods based on equally likely outcomes and experimental evidence as appropriate to find and justify probabilities and approximations these.

1 mark

37. Graph to show how many ice-creams were sold at the fair.

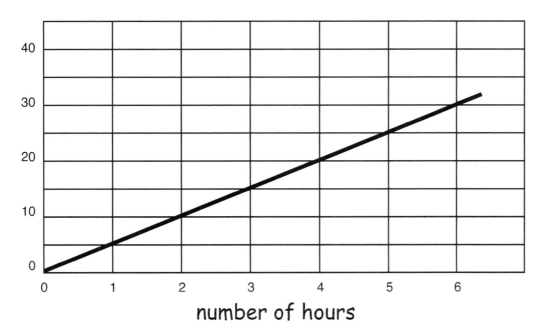

number of hours

How many ice-creams were sold after 3 hours?

Ma4/L5
Processing and representing data
Part D

Create and interpret line graphs where the intermediate values have meaning

1 mark

38.

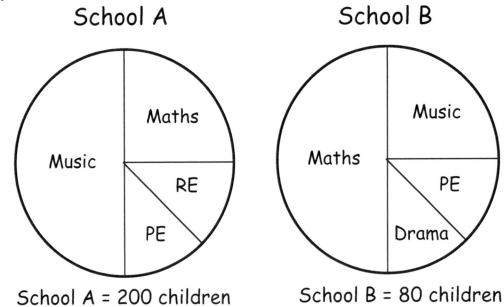

School A   School B

Maths
Music
RE
PE

Music
Maths
PE
Drama

School A = 200 children   School B = 80 children

Sarah says: More children like Maths at school A than school B.

Ma4/L5
Interpreting data
Part B

Interpret graphs and diagrams, including pie charts and draw conclusions

Is she correct? (tick)

Yes ☐   No ☐

1 mark ☐

Explain why _____

_____

_____

_____

1   149, 180, 181, 184, 418

2   3.5, 6, 4.5

3a   Glasgow -10°C

3b   13°C

3c   -3°C

4   29, 21

5   40, 45

6

| 0 | $\frac{1}{4}$ | $\frac{1}{2}$ | | 1 |

7    $\frac{2}{4}$ $\frac{10}{20}$

8   £5.20

9   £18.50

10   8, 7

11   14

12   98

13   16

14   5 x 7 = 35   4 x 4 = 16

15   £2.40

16   30p

17   23

18   24 pens

19   879

20   173

21   70

22   20 ÷ 5 =   8 ÷ 2 =

23   29 ÷ 4 =   17 ÷ 4 =

24

25a

25b

26

27

28   rectangle

29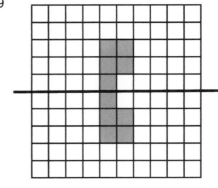

30   anticlockwise

31   7 cm

32   25 minutes

33   360°

34

	Right Angles	No Right Angles
A line of symmetry		✦
No line of symmetry		💬

35   7 children

36   6 children

37   30 children

50

Answers **Year 5 - Level 4**

1	2.5, 2.8, 2.9, 3.1
2	25, 4, 36
3	220, 23900, 232, 35
4	10 pieces
5	1.191, 1.43, 2.5
6	3 girls
7	2
8	6
9	580 - 200 = 380
10	5
11	11
12	8
13	2017

14
32,	18,	21
8,	6,	3
24,	36,	56
8,	6,	7

15	11 girls
16	£2.97
17	100p
18	(1 , 5)
19	352
20	2352
21	79
22	5.1
23	16.91
24	1.8
25	7.5

26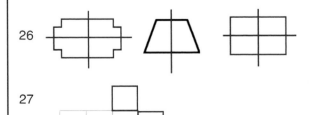

27

28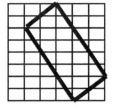

29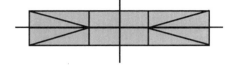

30

31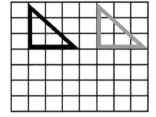

32 *The amount of water in a glass ....millilitres*
    The length of a pencil .....centimetres
    The amount of water in a bath .....litres

33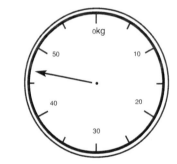

34 Area = 14cm²   Perimeter = 16cm

35 45 minutes

36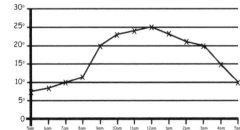

37 6

38 28 children

39 mode = 15   range = 6

1   221, 23920, 23.2, 3.51

2   6, 17

3   1 Oslo, 2 Glasgow, 3 Dublin,
       4 London, 5 Paris, 6 Madrid

4   23, 19

5   No *(Sequence numbers end in*
       4 or 9. 47 ends with a 7)

6    $\frac{1}{2}$ → 50% → 0.5

       $\frac{6}{6}$ → 100% → 1

       $\frac{3}{4}$ → 75% → 0.75

       $\frac{1}{10}$ → 10% → 0.1

7    $\frac{1}{4}$ $\frac{1}{6}$ $\frac{1}{2}$ $\frac{3}{4}$ $\frac{1}{3}$

8    $\frac{1}{4}$ $\frac{1}{3}$ $\frac{1}{2}$

9   300g

10   50, 9

11   40 x 60 = 2400   *or*   30 x 80 = 2400

12   56

13   61°C

14   10,000

15   13.87m

16   22.5

17   38, 26978

18   -40°C

19   42 boys

20   9995 children

21   250 x 100 = 25,000

22   5

23   (-3 , 4)

24   

25   18°

26

27   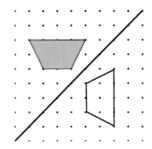

28   e.g.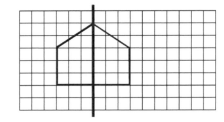

29   e.g.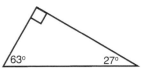

30   reflex angles = 0, obtuse angle = 0
       right angles = 1, acute angles = 2

31   750 ml

32   4400 metres

33   6 cm, 20 cm

34   7

35   0 | | | ↓ | | | 1

36   *Picking a letter B* → Evens
       Picking a letter E → Impossible
       Picking a letter in the 1st half of the alphabet → Certain
       Picking a letter C → Unlikely
       Picking a letter A → Unlikely

37   15

38   Yes *(Maths school A = 50, Maths school B = 40*
       More children like maths in school A)

		APP Mathematics - Gap analysis for group and individual target setting	Names																		
		APP Year 5 Level 3 Date: Group:																				
	Qu.1	**Order numbers up to 1000**																				
	Qu.2	**Use place value to make approximations**																				
	Qu.3a	**Recognise negative temperatures**																				
	Qu.3b	**Recognise negative temperatures**																				
	Qu.3c	**Recognise negative temperatures**																				
	Qu.4	**Recognise a wider range of sequences**																				
	Qu.5	**Recognise a wider range of sequences**																				
	Qu.6	**Place fractions on a number line**																				
	Qu.7	**Recognise equivalent fractions**																				
	Qu.8	**Use decimal notation in money**																				
	Qu.9	**Use decimal notation in money**																				
	Qu.10	**Derive division facts from multiplication facts**																				
A2	Qu.11	**Begin to understand the 'equals' sign**																				
	Qu.12	**Add/subtract 2 digit numbers mentally**																				
	Qu.13	**Add/subtract 2 digit numbers mentally**																				
	Qu.14	**Use mental recall of 2, 3, 4, 5 and 10 x tables**																				
	Qu.15	**Use mental recall of 2, 3, 4, 5 and 10 x tables**																				
	Qu.16	**Use mental recall of add./sub. facts to 20**																				
	Qu.17	**Solve problems with possible remainders**																				
	Qu.18	**Solve problems using multiplication**																				
	Qu.19	**Add/sub. 3 digit numbers in written methods**																				
	Qu.20	**Add/sub. 3 digit numbers in written methods**																				
	Qu.21	**x 2 digit numbers by 2, 3, 4, 5 and 10**																				
	Qu.22	**Divide 2 digit numbers by 2, 3, 4, 5 and 10**																				
	Qu.23	**Divide 2 digit numbers that give remainders**																				
	Qu.24	**Identify 2D shapes with right angles**																				
	Qu.25a	**Classify 2D shapes using math. properties**																				
	Qu.25b	**Classify 2D shapes using math. properties**																				
	Qu.26	**Classify 3D shapes using math. properties**																				
	Qu.27	**Recognise nets of 3D shapes**																				
A3	Qu.28	**Recognise shapes in different orientations**																				
	Qu.29	**Reflect shapes in a mirror line**																				
	Qu.30	**Describe position and movement**																				
	Qu.31	**Use standard and non-standard units**																				
	Qu.32	**Use standard units of time**																				
	Qu.33	**Use a wider range of measures**																				
	Qu.34	**Use a Carroll diagram to sort/classify info.**																				
A4	Qu.35	**Interpret information from bar charts**																				
	Qu.36	**Interpret information from bar charts**																				
	Qu.37	**Interpret information from bar charts**																				

		APP Mathematics - Gap analysis for group and individual target setting																			
		APP Year 5 Level 4 Date: Group:																			
			Names																			
MA2	Qu.1	Recognise and describe number patterns																				
	Qu.2	Recognise and describe square numbers																				
	Qu.3	Use place value to x or ÷ by 10 or 100																				
	Qu.4	Use fractions to describe portions of a whole																				
	Qu.5	Order decimals to 3 decimal places																				
	Qu.6	Begin to understand simple ratio																				
	Qu.7	Use inverse operations																				
	Qu.8	Use inverse operations																				
	Qu.9	Use inverse operations																				
	Qu.10	Use inverse operations																				
	Qu.11	Understand the use of brackets in calculations																				
	Qu.12	Derive division facts from x table facts																				
	Qu.13	Use a range of mental computations																				
	Qu.14	Quickly recall x and ÷ facts up to 10 x 10																				
	Qu.15	Solve problems with/without calculator																				
	Qu.16	Check the reasonableness of results																				
	Qu.17	Begin to use simple word formulae																				
	Qu.18	Use co-ordinates in 1st quadrant																				
	Qu.19	Use efficient written methods for number cal.																				
	Qu.20	Use efficient written methods for number cal.																				
	Qu.21	Use efficient written methods for number cal.																				
	Qu.22	Add/subtract decimals to 2 places																				
	Qu.23	Add/subtract decimals to 2 places																				
	Qu.24	Add/subtract decimals to 2 places																				
	Qu.25	Multiply simple decimal by a single digit																				
MA3	Qu.26	Use the properties of 2D shapes																				
	Qu.27	Make 3D models by linking given faces/edges																				
	Qu.28	Draw 2D shapes in different orientations																				
	Qu.29	Reflect simple shapes in a mirror line																				
	Qu.30	Rotate a shape about its centre																				
	Qu.31	Translate shapes horizontally or vertically																				
	Qu.32	Choose/use appropriate units of measurement																				
	Qu.33	Interpret numbers on measuring instruments																				
	Qu.34	Find areas/perimeters of shapes																				
	Qu.35	Use units of time																				
MA4	Qu.36	Construct simple line graphs																				
	Qu.37	Interpret simple line graphs																				
	Qu.38	Use diagrams to record sorting/classifying																				
	Qu.39	Use mode and range to describe sets of data																				

		APP Mathematics - Gap analysis for group and individual target setting																		
		APP Year 5 Level 5 Date: Group:																		
			Names																		
	Qu.1	x & ÷ whole numbers by 10, 100 and 1000																		
	Qu.2	Round decimals to the nearest decimal place																		
	Qu.3	Order negative temperatures																		
	Qu.4	Recognise prime numbers																		
	Qu.5	Recognise number patterns and relationships																		
	Qu.6	Use equivalence between fractions																		
	Qu.7	Reduce fractions to simplest form																		
	Qu.8	Order fractions and decimals																		
	Qu.9	Understand simple ratio																		
	Qu.10	Use knowledge & operations in calculations																		
	Qu.11	Apply inverse operations																		
A2	Qu.12	Use brackets appropriately																		
	Qu.13	Add/subtract negative numbers in context																		
	Qu.14	Estimate using approximations																		
	Qu.15	Use 4 operations with decimals to 2 places																		
	Qu.16	Use a calculator for fractions/percentages																		
	Qu.17	x or ÷ 3 digit no. by 2 digit no. non-calculator																		
	Qu.18	Problems ordering +/- neg. numbers in context																		
	Qu.19	Problems involving ratio and proportion																		
	Qu.20	Approximate to check answers to problems																		
	Qu.21	Check solutions by applying inverse operations																		
	Qu.22	Use simple formulae involving 1 or 2 operations																		
	Qu.23	Use co-ordinates in 4 quadrants																		
	Qu.24	Use a wider range of 2D and 3D shapes																		
	Qu.25	Sum of a triangle and of angles at a point																		
	Qu.26	Identfy all the symmetries of 2D shapes																		
	Qu.27	Transform shapes																		
A3	Qu.28	Reason about shapes, positions and movement																		
	Qu.29	Measure and draw angles to the nearest degree																		
	Qu.30	Use language associated with angle																		
	Qu.31	Read and interpret scales on instruments																		
	Qu.32	Problems involving conversion of units																		
	Qu.33	Calculate area rectangle/ distinguish perimeter																		
	Qu.34	Understand and use the mean of discrete data																		
	Qu.35	Understand and use the probability scale from 0-1																		
A4	Qu.36	Understand and use probability vocabulary																		
	Qu.37	Interpret intermediate values on line graphs																		
	Qu.38	Interpret graphs, pie charts and diagrams																		